STOCKING STUMPERS
CHRISTMAS 2002
TRIVIA EDITION

**By S. Claus
with help from Russ Edwards and Jack Kreismer**

Red-Letter Press, Inc.

STOCKING STUMPERS: TRIVIA - Christmas 2002 Edition
Copyright ©2002 Red-Letter Press, Inc.
ISBN: 0-940462-28-1
Printed in the United States of America

For information:

Red-Letter Press, Inc.
P.O. Box 393, Saddle River, NJ 07458
www.Red-LetterPress.com

Acknowledgments

A Stocking Stumpers salute to Santa's "subordinate clauses":

Project Development Coordinator: **Kobus Reyneke**

Cover design and typography: **s.w.artz, inc.**

Santa Illustration: **Jack Kreismer, Sr.**

A personal message from Santa

'Twas the night before Christmas
and I left the North Pole
to bring to your stocking
a fresh lump of coal;
But St. Nick's got heart
and your sins weren't voluminous,
so I brought you a gift
in lieu of bituminous;
Now since you've escaped
my long list of lumpers,
I've left you instead
Santa's favorite, *Stocking Stumpers.*

Merry Christmas!

S. Claus

STOCKING STUMPERS
CHRISTMAS 2002
TRIVIA EDITION

FIRST THINGS FIRST

1. Which came first, the car phone or the video camcorder?
2. What are the names of the two storytelling Brothers Grimm?
3. True or false: Limousines are so called because the first one was built by two men, Charles Limous and Thomas Ines.
4. Wrigley chewing gum spearminted, er, spearheaded a trend when it became the first product to be identified in what manner?
5. Who was *Time* magazine's first man of the year?

ANSWERS

1. The first car phone was offered in 1946 while the camcorder didn't appear until 1976.
2. Jacob and Wilhelm
3. False- the vehicle name comes from the area it was first built, the "Limousin" region of France.
4. By a bar code
5. Charles Lindbergh, in 1927

THAT WAS THEN, THIS IS NOW

Santa not only has to make his list and check it twice to see who's naughty or nice, he also has to keep up with changing place names. For the honor of placing the star atop the tree, see if you're current on all the following locales.

1. Constantinople is now ... ?
2. The Sandwich Islands are now ... ?
3. Saigon is now ... ?
4. Abyssinia is now ... ?
5. New Amsterdam is now ... ?

ANSWERS

1. Istanbul
2. The Hawaiian Islands
3. Ho Chi Minh City
4. Ethiopia
5. New York City

PRESIDENTIAL PRODUCTS

1. Which presidential daughter was the model for a popular toy doll sold in stores during her father's administration?
2. This gung-ho chief executive also inspired a classic plush toy.
3. Name the presidential brother who was the inspiration for a new brew.
4. This first lady lent her name to the most famous rehab facility in the world.
5. What candy bar was named after the daughter of President Grover Cleveland?

ANSWERS

1. Caroline Kennedy
2. Teddy Roosevelt (Teddy bear)
3. Billy Carter (Billy Beer)
4. Betty Ford (The Betty Ford Clinic)
5. Baby Ruth

YULETIDE TRIVIA

Can you name the holiday hit Bobby Helms is famous for?

Jingle Bell Rock

WHAT A PIP!

The letters "pip" appear consecutively
in the answers to all of the below.

1. *Midnight Train to Georgia* was one of the many hits that
   drove this Motown group to musical fame.
2. It was a popular musical on Broadway.
3. What are the dots on a pair of dice called?
4. This first baseman was replaced by Lou Gehrig, who then
   went on to play 2,130 consecutive games (a record since
   broken by Cal Ripken Jr. who played in 2,632 straight).
5. He's a basketball forward whose team dominated NBA play
   through the nineties.

ANSWERS

1. Gladys Knight and the Pips
2. *Pippin*
3. Pips
4. Wally Pipp
5. Scottie Pippen

LAKE IT OR NOT

1. What Great Lake is the northernmost *and* westernmost of the great lakes?
2. Garrison Keillor is known for his folksy tales about Lake _____?
3. Where might you find the legendary lake monster known as "Champ?"
4. What states and provinces form the shoreline of Lake Superior?
5. Where did the NBA champion Lakers play their games before moving to Los Angeles?

ANSWERS

1. Lake Superior
2. Wobegon
3. Lake Champlain
4. Michigan, Minnesota, Wisconsin and Ontario
5. Minneapolis, Minnesota (the land of 10,000 lakes)

YULETIDE TALK

"I bought my brother some gift-wrap for Christmas. I took it to
the gift-wrap department and told them to wrap it, but in a
different print so he would know when to stop unwrapping."

-Steven Wright

WHERE IN THE WORLD?

1. You've probably been hitting the old ATM pretty heavily over the holidays but where would you be if you used the Southernmost ATM in the world?
2. If Santa flew high over the world's tallest pyramid, what famous city would be in view?
3. If you're attending the lighting of the Christmas tree on the Ellipse, what city are you in?
4. If you *really* can't wait for Christmas to come, what major nation is the first to celebrate Christmas every year?
5. It's 630 feet by 630 feet and is officially dubbed "The Jefferson National Expansion Monument." Where is it located?

ANSWERS

1. McMurdo Station in Antarctica ... Although there aren't that many people who stay there year 'round, once in a while everybody needs some cold cash!
2. San Francisco ... The Transamerica Pyramid office building is located downtown.
3. Washington D.C.
4. New Zealand ... It lies just west of the International Date Line so it's where Christmas officially begins.
5. St. Louis ... It's the Gateway Arch.

FACT OR FIB?

1. In South American countries, setting off fireworks is a popular way of celebrating Christmas.
2. Abraham Lincoln was a licensed bartender.
3. The potato is a native food of Ireland.
4. *My Country 'Tis of Thee* is the tune of the British national anthem.
5. 7-UP soda got its name from the gambling game of craps.

ANSWERS

1. True
2. True- Lincoln was a co-owner of a saloon called "Berry and Lincoln" in Springfield, Illinois in 1833.
3. False- potatoes originated in Peru and were brought to Europe by explorers.
4. True
5. False- the "7" part stems from when it was created in 1929 and was first sold in seven ounce containers. The "UP" part came from the directions in which the bubbles moved.

SHOW ME THE MONEY

The colors of Christmas are red and green. First you spend
all your green and then you're in the red. Ho! Ho! Ho!
Here's a quick quiz to test your dollars and sense.

1. What was the highest denomination bill ever printed by the
   U.S. government?
2. The paper the dollar bill is printed on is not totally white. It
   has fibers mixed in that are made up of what two colors?
3. The one dollar bill is the most frequently circulated paper
   currency in the U.S. What's second?
4. Whose portrait is on the $50 bill and, for an extra helping of
   plum pudding, what building is pictured on the flip side?
5. True or false? Martha Washington was the only woman ever
   to be featured on a currency note.

ANSWERS

1. $100,000
2. Red and blue
3. The $20 bill
4. U.S. Grant is on the front,
   the U.S. Capitol building is on the back.
5. True

YULETIDE TRIVIA

In what country do they call Father Christmas "Joulupukki"?

Finland

MY WORD!

Match the word with its definition.

1.	celerifere	a)	A type of lizard
2.	piapi	b)	Eighteenth century bicycle/scooter
3.	chuckwalla	c)	Underside of a turtle shell
4.	quidnunc	d)	Busybody
5.	plastron	e)	Hawaaian alphabet

ANSWERS

1. B
2. E
3. A
4. D
5. C

YULETIDE TALK

"I'll tell you what I don't like about Christmas parties:
looking for a new job afterward."

-Phyllis Diller

ADDRESS THE ISSUE

Which famous TV characters/shows would Santa
be delivering gifts to if he wriggled down the chimney
at the following addresses?

1. 328 Chauncey Street in Brooklyn, New York
2. 742 Evergreen Terrace
3. 342 Gravelpit Terrace
4. 90 Bedford Street in Greenwich Village
5. 10 Stigwood Avenue, Brooklyn Heights

ANSWERS

1. *The Honeymooners*
2. *The Simpsons*
3. *The Flintstones*
4. *Friends*
5. *The Cosby Show*

HOLIDAY HO-HO-HOS!

It's time to take a stumpers break with these groaners from the North Pole's resident jokester, Henny Elfman.

1. How do sheep in Mexico say Merry Christmas?
2. Why was Santa's helper down in the dumps?
3. Where do polar bears vote?
4. What do you get when you cross an archer with a Christmas gift-wrapper?
5. Why does Scrooge love Rudolph?

ANSWERS

1. "Fleece Navidad"
2. Because he had low elf-esteem
3. At the North Poll
4. Ribbon Hood
5. Because every buck is deer to him

YULETIDE TALK

"My sons call me Scrooge. Santa never visits my house, and the chimney is plugged up ... But I did do half a good deed this year. I helped an old lady halfway across the street of a very busy thoroughfare."

-Zero Mostel

TIME AND TIME AGAIN

1. Is Thanksgiving always on the last Thursday of November?
2. What is 1/60 of 1/60 of 1/24 of a day?
3. True or false? Any month that starts on a Sunday will have a Friday the 13th.
4. Here's a trivia teaser: "Two days ago I was 69 years old. Next year, I'll be 72." How can someone make that statement?
5. What's the longest month of the year?

ANSWERS

1. No- it's on the fourth Thursday of the month.
2. One second
3. True
4. This can only be said about someone who is born on December 31 and is saying that on January 1.
5. October- when the clocks are moved back an hour to Daylight Standard Time, the month becomes 31 days and 1 hour long.

YULETIDE TALK

"If you think The Nutcracker is something you did off the high-dive, you might be a redneck."

-Jeff Foxworthy

LOONY LAWS

Which of the following laws are, or were, regulations?

1. In Washington, D.C., it's illegal to fly a kite.
2. You're not permitted to ride an ugly horse in Wilbur, Washington.
3. In Alabama, it's illegal to play dominoes on Sunday.
4. In California, you're prohibited from sleeping in the kitchen; however, it is okay to cook in the bedroom.
5. It's against the law to put a skunk in your boss' desk in Michigan.

ANSWERS

They are all true. Speaking of law, did you know that the U.S. has 5% of the world's population and 70% of its lawyers?

That reminds Santa of a joke: The American Bar Association was having its annual convention at the Marriott Hotel in New York. All of the biggies were there - Johnny Cochrane, Marcia Clark, F. Lee Bailey and so on. Suddenly, the hotel was raided by terrorists who held the lawyers hostage. They let their demands be known through the media. They also let it be known that until their demands were met, they would release one lawyer an hour. Ho ho ho!

'TEN-HUT!

Santa invites you to snap your mind to attention
with these military mindbenders.

1. Who was captain of the *Jolly Roger*?
2. Who was Harland Sanders?
3. His real name was Charles Stratton but you know this
   diminutive general better as ... ?
4. Who was Sgt. Bilko's (played by Phil Silvers) post
   commander?
5. In order to become Commander-in-Chief of the United
   States, there are three major considerations. Number one -
   you must be a natural born citizen of the U.S. Number two -
   you must be at least 35 years of age. What is number three?

ANSWERS

1. Captain Hook - whose first name, by the way, is James
2. The Kentucky Fried Chicken colonel
3. 36-inch-tall P.T. Barnum employee, General Tom Thumb
4. Colonel Hall
5. You must be elected! (That is, of course, barring a replacement of a president removed from office for whatever reason.)

THE RED, WHITE AND BLUE

Let's run these questions up the flagpole
and see if anyone salutes.

1. When Francis Scott Key wrote the *Star Spangled Banner*,
   how many stripes did the U.S. flag have?
2. On the current U.S. flag, are there more red or white
   stripes?
3. An expert in the history of flags is a: a) piscatologist
   b) spermologist c) numismatist d) vexillologist
4. What do the terms "hoist" and "fly" refer to?
5. True or false? The colors of Old Glory have no particular
   significance.

ANSWERS

1. 15, representing the amount of states at the time
2. The reds win, 7 to 6.
3. D ... A piscatologist is a specialist in the study of fish; a numismatist is a coin expert; and a spermologist, believe it or not, is a trivia buff.
4. The hoist is the attached side of the flag while the fly is the body of it.
5. False ... Red stands for heartiness and valor; white symbolizes purity and innocence; and blue is for vigilance and perseverance.

THE FEAR OF IT

Combine the word with the phobia description.

1. Astraphobia
2. Cynophobia
3. Glossophobia
4. Musophobia
5. Logizomechanophobia

a) Fear of speaking in public
b) Fear of mice
c) Fear of computers (or machines)
d) Fear of dogs
e) Fear of lightning and thunder

ANSWERS

1. E
2. D
3. A
4. B
5. C

YULETIDE TRIVIA

In 1875, Louis Prang introduced a custom to America that is still popular to this day. Any idea what it is?

He began the tradition of sending Christmas cards.

PHRASE CRAZE

See if you can figure out what items these phrases represent.

1. OholeNE

2. MIND
   MATTER

3. T
   O
   U
   C
   H

4. R
   E
   K
   C
   U
   P

5. COF FEE

ANSWERS

1. Hole in one
2. Mind over matter
3. Touchdown
4. Pucker up
5. Coffee break

YULETIDE TALK

"Nothing destroys the Christmas spirit faster than looking
for a place to park."

-Anonymous

WHAT WOULD YOU DO WITH ... ?

If you think what to do with Aunt Erma's fruitcake is a problem,
whatever would you do with the following gifts?

1. Jerkin, Chaddar, Kirtie, Caftan?
2. Blini, Brioche, Mulligatawny, Stilton?
3. Bugatti, Lamborghini, Duesenberg, Karmann Ghia?
4. Talent, Jitney, Farthing, Pfenning?
5. Roman a clef, homily, Haiku, Dossier?

ANSWERS

1. You'd wear them. They're all clothes items.
2. You'd eat them. They're food items.
3. You'd drive them. They are types of cars.
4. You'd spend them. They're forms of currency.
5. You'd read them. They're all reading material.

YULETIDE TALK

"The ideal Christmas present is money. The only trouble is you can't charge it."

-Bill Vaughan

WHAT'S IN A NAME?

1. What's the main difference between the design of Boulder Dam and Hoover Dam?
2. Although most of the world knows it by another name, what country calls itself "Kalatdlit-Nunat?"
3. This sentence has four "tittles" in it. What are they?
4. Chances are you don't know what an "ideo locator" is but surely you've seen one. What is it?
5. What are"Botz Dots?"

ANSWERS

1. Ho ho ho! There is none. They're just two names for the same dam thing.
2. Greenland
3. The dots over the "i's."
4. The "You are here" arrow on a map
5. They're the raised reflective bumps in the middle of the road.

YULETIDE TALK

"Anyone who thinks Christmas doesn't last all year
doesn't have a charge account."

-Anonymous

MISCELLANEOUS MINDBENDERS

1. Who coined the phrase "Crime does not pay?"
   a) Herbert Hoover b) Robert F. Kennedy c) Chester Gould
   d) Elliott Gould

2. See if you can clean up on this one ... What word has consecutive u's?

3. Who's the only person to serve in both the American Revolution and the War of 1812?

4. Can you name four words in the English language which end in "dous?"

5. Here's one that's elementary: What was Sherlock Holmes' assistant's first name?

ANSWERS

1. C ... Gould wrote those words which were said by his comic strip character, Dick Tracy.
2. Vacuum
3. Andrew Jackson
4. Horrendous, hazardous, stupendous and tremendous
5. John, my dear Watson

YULETIDE TRIVIA

Which one of Santa's reindeer is female?

Vixen

TEASER TIME-OUT

Santa can't resist including some brain teasers in Stocking
Stumpers, so take another break from the trivia toughies
and try your hand at the puzzles below.

1. What's in the middle of nowhere?
2. What's unique about the following sentence? Bores are
   people that say people are bores.
3. How far can one of Santa's reinder run into the woods?
4. Add one letter to make the following complete: SMTWTF_.
5. What has a foot on each side and one in the middle?

ANSWERS

1. The letter "h"
2. It's a "pseudodrome" - a phrase in which the words read the same forwards and backwards.
3. Halfway- after that, the deer's running out.
4. The letter "S" completes the first letter of each day of the week.
5. A yardstick

WHO SAID IT?

1. "This man I was going with asked me for my finger measurements. I thought he was going to buy me a ring for Christmas, but he gave me a bowling ball." a) Rita Rudner b) Phyllis Diller c) Elizabeth Taylor d) Lawrence Taylor

2. "Santa Claus has the right idea - visit people once a year." a) Victor Borge b) Sally Field c) Steve Martin d) Ricky Martin

3. "My kids love to get money for Christmas because it's always the right size." a) Donald Trump b) Ebenezer Scrooge c) Uncle Scrooge d) Uncle Miltie

4. "Two weeks before Christmas, I always think of a good gift for someone, but it has to be ordered three weeks in advance." a) Andy Rooney b) Jay Leno c) Paul Newman d) Alfred E. Neuman

5. "I wish all my friends a Merry Christmas except two." a) W.C. Fields b) Howard Stern c) Rich Little d) Little Richard

ANSWERS

1. B
2. A
3. D (Milton Berle)
4. A
5. A

SHOW BIZ STUMPERS

1. On the sitcom *Seinfeld*, what was George's ATM password?
2. As a little girl she was on Santa's Christmas list as Caryn Johnson but you know her better as _____?
3. In the 1970s, millions of people responded to almost anything with "Heeeeyyy!" What TV character started this craze?
4. What Hollywood "fame" do the following characters have in common? Mickey Mouse, Woody Woodpecker, Bugs Bunny and Snow White
5. What early children's TV show had the young audience seated in the "Peanut Gallery?"

ANSWERS

1. Bosco
2. Whoopi Goldberg
3. Fonzie, on *Happy Days*
4. They are the only fictional characters with stars on Hollywood's Walk of Fame. (There are a couple of dogs, too - Lassie and Rin Tin Tin.)
5. *Howdy Doody*

YULETIDE TALK

"I love Christmas. I get lots of wonderful presents I can't wait to exchange."

-Kathleen Knight

INITIALLY SPEAKING

Your job here is to fill in the words that match the number. For instance, 7 = d. in a w. becomes 7 = days in a week.

1. 13 = o. U.S. c.
2. 12 = m. in a y.
3. 26 = l. of the a.
4. 73 = h.r. by B. B.
5. 8 = s. to an o.
6. 366 = d. in a l. y.
7. 8 = a. on an o.
8. 88 = k. on a p.
9. 12 = d. of C.
10. 9 = S. r. (including R.)

ANSWERS

1. 13 = original U.S. colonies
2. 12 = months in a year
3. 26 = letters of the alphabet
4. 73 = home runs by Barry Bonds
5. 8 = sides to an octagon
6. 366 = days in a leap year
7. 8 = arms on an octopus
8. 88 = keys on a piano
9. 12 = days of Christmas
10. 9 = Santa's reindeer (including Rudolph)

BABY TALK

1. "Babies are our business" is the advertising slogan of what company?
2. Do you know Babe Ruth's first and middle names?
3. Who was the radio voice of Baby Snooks? (Hint: A Broadway musical based on her life became the film *Funny Girl*.)
4. What was the last line of many of *The Honeymooners* episodes?
5. Super stumper: What's the title of the self-help book written by psychiatrist Dr. Leo Marvin (played by Richard Dreyfuss) in the film *What About Bob*?

ANSWERS

1. Gerber baby food
2. George Herman
3. Fanny Brice
4. *"Baby, you're the greatest!"*
5. *Baby Steps*

YULETIDE TALK

"Christmas shopper- a shlock absorber."

-*Sanford Mims*

LETTER-PERFECT

Identify what the letters stand for in the quiz below.

1. WD-40
2. LLCoolJ
3. B.F. Goodrich
4. *The Man from U.N.C.L.E.*
5. CD-ROM

ANSWERS

1. Water Displacement
2. Ladies Love Cool James
3. Benjamin Franklin
4. United Network Command for Law Enforcement
5. Compact Disk-Read Only Memory

YULETIDE TRIVIA

Who wrote The Gift of the Magi?

O. Henry

BRIGHT IDEAS

Sure, we've all heard about inventors like Edison and Bell,
but there are many more unsung creative geniuses.
For an extra dip in the eggnog bowl at the Christmas party,
match the inventor and the invention.

1.	Frederick Rohwedder	a)	Postage stamp
2.	Sylvan Goldman	b)	Automatic Teller Machine
3.	Douglas Engelbart	c)	First computer mouse
4.	Sir Rowland Hill	d)	Bread slicer
5.	Don Wetzel	e)	Shopping cart

ANSWERS

1. D - and most folks thought it was the greatest thing since sliced bread.
2. E
3. C
4. A
5. B

DON'T KNOW MUCH ABOUT HISTORY?

Check and see with this quick quiz on U.S. Presidents.

1. Who was the first president to wear long pants?
2. Who was the only man to have been vice-president and president yet was never elected to either office?
3. Who was the last president to be elected by all-male voters?
4. Which American presidents are not buried in the United States?
5. What president was in office when the first telephone was installed at the White House?

ANSWERS

1. James Madison ... Before him all the presidents wore knee britches. In a few recent cases it's been rumored that it was the First Lady who wore the pants in the White House.
2. Gerald Ford
3. Woodrow Wilson ... The Nineteenth Amendment to the U.S. Constitution states that the right to vote shall not be denied because of sex. This amendment was first proposed in 1919 and was ratified in August 1920, just prior to the 1920 election of Warren G. Harding.
4. Why the ones who are still alive of course- ho, ho, ho!
5. Grover Cleveland was in office when the first telephone rang and he answered it himself.

SEASONAL STUMPERS

1. What's the single largest Christmas tree exporting region in the world?

2. What do Little Richard, Barbara Mandrell and Sissy Spacek share in common?

3. If your true love followed the lyrics of *The Twelve Days of Christmas*, how many birds could you expect to get?

4. *Auld Lang Syne* is a favorite of Santa's. Just what does "auld lang syne" mean?

5. In Switzerland, what do they call Santa's wife?
   a) Gerda b) Lucy c) Tanta Kringle d) Frau Christenklinger

ANSWERS

1. Novia Scotia
2. They were all born on Christmas Day.
3. 184
4. It's Scottish for "old long ago."
5. B ... And to quote Desi Arnaz - I love Lucy!

YULETIDE TRIVIA

The poinsettia comes from what country?

Mexico

ANIMAL ACTS

1. Which lives longer, a chipmunk or an opossum?
2. Which of these animals runs the fastest?
   a) Rabbit b) Squirrel c) Elephant d) Grizzly bear
3. What do you call a group of swans?
4. What is the world's largest animal?
5. You might not think this question fits the category, but Santa can't resist ... Introduced to America in 1902 by the National Biscuit Company, its box's carrying string was designed for hanging on a Christmas tree. What's the product?

ANSWERS

1. A chipmunk, with an average life span of 6 years ...
   An opossum's life span is just one year.
2. A ... A rabbit runs an average of 35 miles per hour;
   a squirrel, 12 mph; an elephant, 25 mph; and a grizzly
   bear approximately 30 mph.
3. A bevy
4. The blue whale (110 feet long, 209 tons)
5. Animal Crackers

HOLIDAY HO-HO-HOS!

Once again, let's take a trivia time-out with another round of groaners from Santa's sidekick, Henny Elfman.

1. Why did the elf put his bed into the fireplace?
2. What did one of Santa's elves put on the Internet?
3. How would you fire Santa?
4. What nationality is Santa?
5. What do they have for breakfast at the North Pole?

ANSWERS

1. He wanted to sleep like a log.
2. A gnome page
3. Give him the sack.
4. North Polish
5. Snowflakes

POTPOURRI

1. Cartoonist Thomas Nast is credited with creating the modern version of Santa Claus. In these days of being politically correct, what two famous animals did he create?
2. The act of snapping one's fingers is called a:
   a) fillip b) bezel c) callithump d) haruspex
3. How big is a "two-by-four" piece of wood?
4. What product was originally called "Little Short-Cake Fingers"?
5. Matinees are generally afternoon events. The word "matinee" is French for what meaning?

ANSWERS

1. The donkey for the Democratic Party and the elephant for the Republicans
2. A
3. 1 1/2 inches by 3 1/2 inches
4. Twinkies
5. Morning

YULETIDE TRIVIA

What was Brenda Lee's "rockin'" Christmas song?

"Rockin' Around the Christmas Tree"

AUTO BIOGRAPHIES

1. What do the letters M.G. on the British car stand for?
2. The Nash was the first automobile to sport seat belts. In what year?
   a) 1950 b) 1960 c) 1970 d) 1980
3. When Sir Henry Royce died in 1933 the manufacturers changed the monogram from red to what color?
4. Where would you commonly see letters in this order: ECNALUBMA?
5. Why wasn't the Chevrolet Nova a popular car in Mexico?

ANSWERS

1. Morris Garage
2. A
3. Black
4. On the front of an ambulance (It's reversed so that, when you look in your rear view mirror while driving, it reads as though it's spelled forward.)
5. Nova means "won't go" in Spanish.

CLOCKWORK

1. What is the third hand on a clock called?
2. An extremely odd happenstance occurred in 1978 on the 6th of May at 12:34 p.m. Do you know what it is?
3. When is the only time (remember, Santa's talking time here) you can add five to eleven and have the solution be four?
4. What manufacturer's timepiece is seen in the opening of *60 Minutes* each week?
5. If an event occurred semidiurnally, how often would that be?

ANSWERS

1. The second hand
2. At that exact moment, the time read 12:34, 5/6/78.
3. If you were to tack on five hours to eleven o'clock, the time would be four o'clock.
4. Aristo's
5. Twice a day

THE NAME GAME

1. According to the Boat Owners Association of the U.S., what is the most popular name given to boats?
2. What is Paul McCartney's first name?
3. It was originally called Wired Radio Inc., but you know it better by what name?
4. What were the nicknames of Old West outlaws Robert Parker and Harry Longabaugh?
5. Organized crime is called Yakuza in this country. Where in the world is this?

ANSWERS

1. Odyssey
2. James
3. Muzak
4. Butch Cassidy and the Sundance Kid
5. Japan

I-OPENERS

The answers to all of these questions begin with the letter "I."

1. What English word has six "i's" in it?
2. On Tuesday, May 30, 1911 Ray Harroun won what inaugural race with a speed of 74.59 miles per hour?
3. Do you remember the slogan for a Peter Paul candy bar?
4. What was Chevy Chase's opening line as host of the "Weekend Update" segment of TV's *Saturday Night Live*?
5. What was the former name of John F. Kennedy International Airport in New York City?

ANSWERS

1. Indivisibility
2. The Indianapolis 500
3. Indescribably delicious
4. "I'm Chevy Chase, and you're not."
5. Idlewild

YULETIDE TALK

"If I worked behind the counter of a store that played Christmas music over its loudspeakers, I'd want to be paid extra for having to listen to it. There are just so many times anyone can stand to hear *Jingle Bells*, *Rudolph the Red-Nosed Reindeer*, or even *Silent Night*."

-Andy Rooney

MATCHMAKER, MATCHMAKER

Link the celebrity couples who are, or were, together.
The catch here is that the famous female is either
listed by her original or maiden name.

1. Roy Rogers
2. Dennis Quaid
3. Gerald Ford
4. Frank Gifford
5. Desi Arnaz

a) Elizabeth Bloomer
b) Kathie Epstein
c) Francis Octavia Smith
d) Dianne Belmont
e) Margaret Hyra

ANSWERS

1. C (Dale Evans)
2. E (Meg Ryan)
3. A (Betty Ford)
4. B (Kathy Lee Gifford)
5. D (Lucille Ball)

SECOND GUESSING

1. Statistics show that Cinco De Mayo is the biggest day for Americans to eat avocados. How about the second biggest avocado-eating occasion?
2. Delaware became the first state in the U.S. Which state was second?
3. William H. Harrison had the shortest term of office as U.S. president. Who had the second shortest term?
4. Before 1900, the Eiffel Tower, at 984 feet, was the world's tallest structure. What was second?
5. The U.S., by far, has the most telephones. Which country is second?

ANSWERS

1. Super Bowl Sunday
2. Pennsylvania
3. James Garfield - 199 days
4. The Washington Monument - 555 feet
5. Japan

YULETIDE TRIVIA

What is the state flower of Oklahoma?

Mistletoe

NATIVE TONGUES

True or false?

1. The language of South Africa is Afrikaans.
2. Marinien is the language used in San Marino.
3. In Malta, the predominant language is Esperanto.
4. The offical language of Monaco is French.
5. Bengali is the official language of Bangladesh.

ANSWERS

1. True
2. False - it's Italian.
3. False - it's Maltese.
4. True
5. True

YULETIDE TALK

"An unemployed Santa is a ho-ho-hobo."

-Jay Kaye

MISCELLANEOUS MINDBENDERS

1. What fine feathered friend, whose middle name is Fauntleroy, made his film debut in a 1934 cartoon called *The Wise Little Hen*?

2. What ill-fated automobile was named after Henry Ford's only child?

3. For what movie could you say that Santa Claus won an Academy Award?

4. How did red and green become the traditional colors of Christmas?

5. How did hearing-plagued inventor Thomas Edison propose to his future wife?

ANSWERS

1. Donald Duck
2. The Edsel
3. *Miracle on 34th Street*, in which Edmund Gwenn won the Oscar for his portrayal of Ol' St. Nick
4. In early times, Christmas tree decorations consisted of red apples on the green tree.
5. In Morse Code - She repled, "Yes," also in Morse Code.

TEASER TIME-OUT

Okay, time for one more breather with these mind bogglers before we hit the Stocking Stumpers home stretch.

1. She's your uncle's sister but she isn't legally your aunt. Who can she be?
2. It's a little known fact that Donder and Blitzen were born the same day - to the same parents. They look exactly alike and yet they are not twins. How's that possible?
3. Before Mt. Everest was discovered, what was the largest mountain in the world?
4. What question can you ask all day long, always get a different answer, and yet all the answers could be correct?
5. What's the only thing you can put in a bucket that will make it lighter?

ANSWERS

1. Your mother
2. They are two of a set of triplets.
3. It was still Mt. Everest. It just hadn't been discovered yet!
4. "What time is it?"
5. A hole

YULETIDE TALK

"Dashing through the dough."

-Ralph M. Wyser

WHICH CAME FIRST ...

1. Rubber bands or band-aids?
2. The first African-American to win an Olympic gold medal or the first African-American to break baseball's color barrier?
3. The American Express credit card or the Diner's Club card?
4. The Frisbee or the Hula Hoop?
5. The first female Supreme Court Justice or the first female TV news anchor?

ANSWERS

1. Rubber bands, in 1845 - Johnson and Johnson's band-aid cut the ribbon in 1920.
2. The gold medal winner was first - Jesse Owens in 1936. Jackie Robinson became the first big league African-American baseball player in 1947.
3. The Diner's Club card, in 1950 - American Express came along in 1958.
4. The Frisbee, in 1957 - The Hula Hoop came a year later.
5. The first TV anchor, Barbara Walters, in 1976 - Sandra Day O'Connor became the first female Supreme Court Justice in 1981.

FACT OR FIB?

Santa expects everyone to tell the truth but some good-natured fibbing can be fun. See how good a lie detector you are.

1. Moby Dick was based on a real whale.
2. Rap artist Jay-Z's real name is Zane Jay.
3. The Backstreet Boys band is made up of former Mouseketeers.
4. The design of the Space Shuttle was chosen by Richard Nixon.
5. The name "United States of America" was coined by Benjamin Franklin.

ANSWERS

1. True
2. False - his real name is Shawn Carter. He grew up in Brooklyn, NY near the J and Z subway lines; hence, his stage name.
3. False
4. True
5. False - Thomas Paine came up with the good old U.S. of A's name.

ACRONYMANIA

What do the following stand for?

1. CAT (scan)
2. NECCO
3. SNAFU
4. YUPPY
5. GIGO

ANSWERS

1. **C**omputerized **A**xial **T**omography
2. **N**ew **E**ngland **C**onfectionary **Co**mpany (as in the candy)
3. **S**ituation **N**ormal **A**ll **F**ouled **U**p
4. **Y**oung **U**rban **P**rofessional (with a diminutive ending as a pet name, e.g. "Johnny")
5. **G**arbage **I**n, **G**arbage **O**ut

SEASONAL STUMPERS

1. What's the most popular tree topper?
2. James Pierpont gave the world a wonderful gift when he wrote what beloved Christmas standard?
3. Which one of the reindeer is never mentioned in *The Night Before Christmas*?
4. What's the only Christmas decoration ever banned by the government?
5. Who named the Chipmunks in their 1958 Christmas Song?

ANSWERS

1. An angel
2. *Jingle Bells*
3. Rudolph
4. Tinsel ... It used to contain lead which is very poisonous. Nowadays, it's made of plastic and the worst you can get from it is a bad case of tinselitis ... Ho ho ho!
5. Performer and songwriter David Seville- Alvin and Simon were named for two executives at Liberty Records, Al Bennett and Simon Waronker. Theodore was named for the recording engineer, Ted Keep.

Merry Christmas!